Patrick McDonnell's cartoons have appeared in *The New York Magazine, Time, People, Sports Illustrated* and several other American magazines. He is the co-author of *Krazy Kat: The Comic Art of George Herriman.*

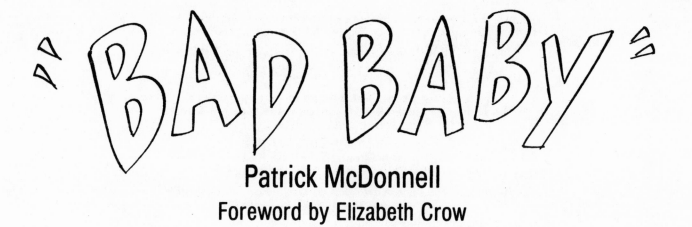

"BAD BABY"

Patrick McDonnell

Foreword by Elizabeth Crow

CENTURY
LONDON SYDNEY AUCKLAND JOHANNESBURG

Thanks to *Parents* magazine, Elizabeth Crow, Cliff Gardiner, Richard Loretoni, Deirdre Costa Major, Robert McDonnell and Kevin O'Connell.

First published in 1989 by Century Hutchinson Ltd,
Brookmount House, 62-65 Chandos Place, Covent Garden,
London WC2N 4NW

Century Hutchinson Australia Pty Limited,
89-91 Albion Street, Surry Hills, Sydney,
New South Wales 2010, Australia

Century Hutchinson New Zealand Limited, PO Box 40-086,
Glenfield, Auckland 10, New Zealand

Century Hutchinson South Africa (Pty) Ltd, PO Box 337,
Bergvlei, 2012 South Africa

Printed and bound in Great Britain by
Scotprint Ltd, Musselburgh

British Library Cataloguing in Publication Data

McDonnell, Patrick
Bad baby.
1. American humorous strip-cartoons
I. Title
741.5'973
ISBN 0-7126-3055-4

FOREWORD

When Patrick McDonnell created "Bad Baby" for *Parents* in 1984, lots of things happened—all of them good. Mothers and fathers loved this true-to-life spoof. And if babies could read, I'm sure their reactions would be even more exuberant.

Of course, the title is a misnomer. There's no such thing as a bad baby. Babies are never bad. Amusing, adorable, ineffable, and even mysterious, but never bad. They're simply babies.

Now that Patrick McDonnell has collected his wonderfully funny drawings in a book, parents can reap the benefit. What is the benefit? Actually there are two: *"Bad Baby"* will help parents relax about their baby's perfectly normal behavior. And it will give them a chance to laugh their heads off. That's more than worth the cover price.

Elizabeth Crow
Former Editor-in-Chief
Parents Magazine

BAD BABY

Patrick McDonnell ©1985.

BAD BABY "DREAMS ARE MADE OF THIS"

Bad Baby

IN

"Fashion Plate"

WHAT ARE the "IN" bad babies WEARING this YEAR?

THEIR BREAKFAST.

THE LATEST DESSERTS FROM PARIS.

AND HERE'S A CUTE FELLOW SPORTING A BIG SMILE FOR MOM.

PATRICK MC DONNELL

—PATRICK M^cDONNELL

BAD BABY — BY PATRICK McDONNELL

DON'T WANNA GO TO SCHOOL. BAWWW

BAWW

WAAAH WE DON'T WANT TO! :BORSH:

WAAAHH

HEY! YOU DON'T EVEN GO TO SCHOOL.

WAAH BAAWW

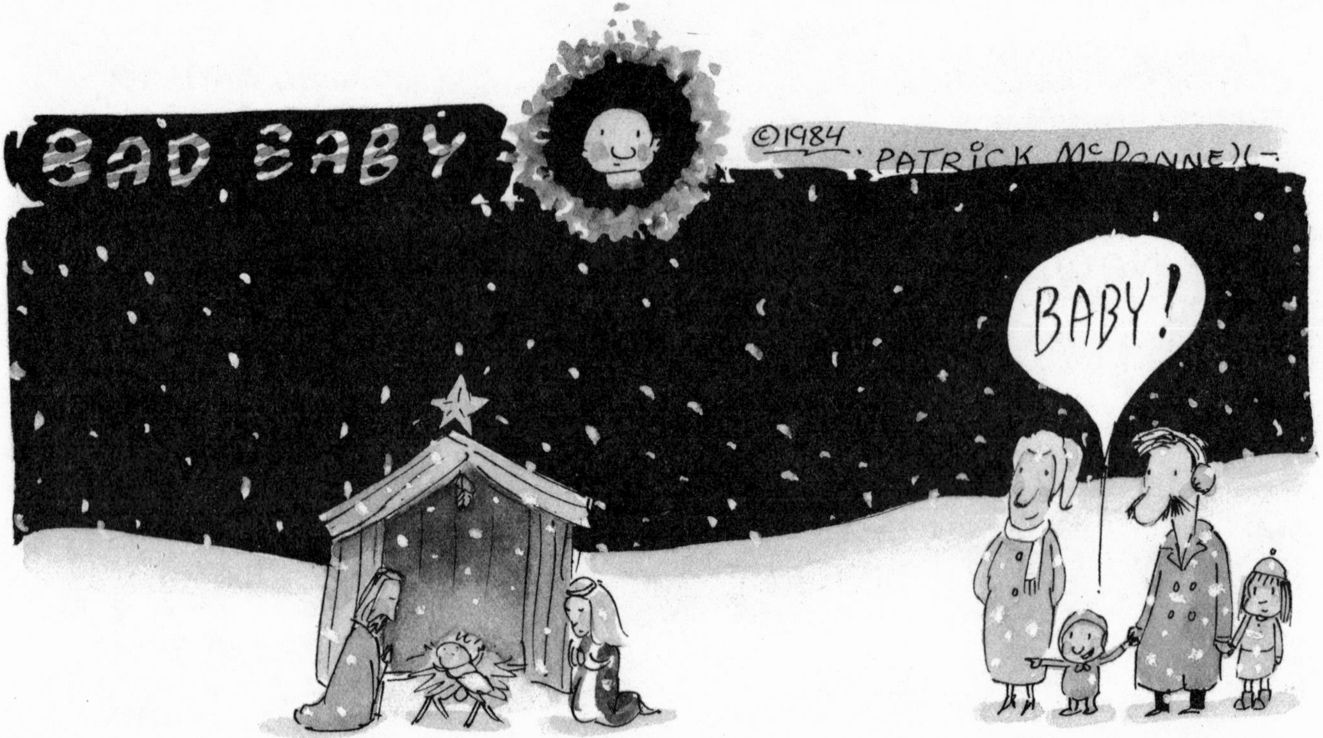
BAD BABY
©1984 PATRICK McDONNELL
BABY!

"BAD BABY'S
BED TIME
STORIES

©1985 by PATRICK McDONNELL

"BABY"
HAD A
LITTLE
BLANKY

IT
WAS
FULL
O'
HOLES

EVERYWHERE
THAT "BABY"
WENT...

IT
WAS SURE
TO GO.

"BAD BABY" ~~~~ by PATRICK McDONNELL ©1988.

the GOOD... the BAD... AND THE UGLY.

BAD BABY Theatre presents "FIRST STEPS"

PLOP

· CHOREOGRAPHED BY ·PATRICK McDONNELL ©1985·

BAD BABY MARCH
BY. PATRICK McDONNELL ©1987.
IN LIKE A LION....
OUT LIKE A LAMB.
Z
Z
Z
Z

...AND THEN THE EASTER BUNNY PLACES ALL THE PAINTED EGGS IN A BIG BASKET AND HOPS TO ALL THE BOYS AND GIRLS' HOMES.

"BAD BABY" BY PATRICK McDONNELL ©1987

I DON'T THINK HE'S BUYING IT.

"BAD BABY" IN BUTTER-FLY BAWL.

©1986 PATRICK McDonnell

"BAD BABY"

©1987 BY PATRICK McDONNELL·

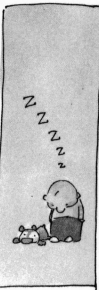

"BAD BABY" UPDATE . . . . BY PATRICK McDONNELL ©1987

THE WORLD REMAINS HIS PLAYTHING....

APPLE JUICE STILL THE FAVORITE...

MR BLANKET IS NOW MR STRING......

STAY TUNED FOR ANY FURTHER DEVELOPMENTS...